MW00619539

"If our leaders are not passionately driven by the right beliefs, we are headed for disaster. At the same time, if believers cannot lead, we are headed nowhere. In his book, *Through Colored Glasses*, Tom Harper mixes right beliefs and leadership skill. His thoughtful, engaging presentation of biblical leadership is a sorely needed message for Christians in leadership positions, both in the workplace and in the church."

R. Albert Mohler, Jr., President of the
Southern Baptist Theological Seminary

"Leaders lead people, not organizations. Tom Harper brings this out brilliantly in his new book, *Through Colored Glasses*. This engaging, contextual leadership parable will enlighten you about what happens behind the scenes, when people attempt to lead others."

Dr. Richard Blackaby, president of Blackaby Ministries
International, and author of *Spiritual Leadership*
and *Living Out of the Overflow*

"Understanding and defining reality requires leaders to be truth seekers and tellers. This book illustrates the power of truth and the spiritual insight that the Bible provides to guide leadership."

David Novak, co-founder of Yum! Brands and author of
Taking People with You and *O Great One*

"Infusing Patrick Lencioni's leadership fable motif with marketplace discipleship, Tom Harper's *Through Colored Glasses* encourages business leaders who follow Christ to realize their impact at work. A weary CEO, a mutinous CFO, a consultant, and a praying manager meet at the intersection of faith and corporate America, demonstrating how biblical witness is effective even in difficult places."

Thom S. Rainer, president and CEO of LifeWay
Christian Resources and best-selling author of
I Am a Church Member and *Simple Church*

"Tom Harper combines story, time-tested principles, and innovative ideas to help leaders see and conquer tomorrow's challenges. You will be absorbed by the fast-paced story and biblical insights that can transform your leadership."

Bob Whitesel, PhD, award-winning author,
consultant, and founding professor of Wesley Seminary
at Indiana Wesleyan University

"In Tom Harper's latest book, *Through Colored Glasses*, his fast-paced parable takes you into the leadership struggles men and women face every day. You witness the strongholds of pride and fear and how the sin of both distorts thinking and doing. But God knows the motivation of the heart and always presents a way home. Truly a perfect book for anyone in leadership as it has the power to both encourage and convict."

Tami Heim, president and CEO
of Christian Leadership Alliance

"In his intriguing book, *Through Colored Glasses: How Great Leaders Reveal Reality*, Tom Harper presents a fable that is sure to capture your imagination while prompting serious thoughts about your effectiveness as a leader. Your philosophy and practice of leadership will never be the same."

Bob Russell, retired senior pastor, Southeast Christian
Church, and author of *After 50 Years of Ministry:
7 Things I'd Do Differently and 7 Things I'd Do the Same*

"Tom Harper has taken an easy-to-read leadership fable and not only helped us with leadership, but turned it into a powerful teaching about life."

Ron Edmondson, pastor and author
of *The Mythical Leader*

"Leading people can be tough work, especially when we don't know their motives, beliefs, and biases. Tom's book is a clever tale that delivers a profound lesson. You'll not only be engaged by the easy-to-read story, but you'll gain new insights on how to understand the people you're called to lead."

Kent Evans, author of *Wise Guys: Unlocking Hidden
Wisdom From the Men Around You*

"The Holy Scriptures provide timeless principles on leadership. In his book *Through Colored Glasses*, Tom Harper brings those biblical principles to life in a moving parable that illustrates the power of humility in leadership and the impact of turning your business over to God."

Mark Deterding, author of *Leading Jesus' Way*

THROUGH COLORED GLASSES

HOW GREAT LEADERS REVEAL REALITY

Tom R. Harper

A Biblical Leadership Fable

Through Colored Glasses:
How Great Leaders Reveal Reality
Tom R. Harper
Copyright © 2018 by Tom R. Harper

DeepWater Books
13100 Eastpoint Park Blvd.
Louisville, KY 40223

Printed in the United States of America

ISBN 978-0-9994671-0-7

For Kate—

my daughter
who loves to create

and who was created
to love

INTRODUCTION

If there is any one secret of success, it lies in the ability to get the other person's point of view and see things from that person's angle as well as from your own.

—Henry Ford

It's hard to know what's real these days.

If you read different news media outlets, you probably notice distinctly different views of the same occurrence—especially if it's political. Bias has become so obvious I've made a pastime out of flipping between various news sites to marvel at the masterful spin.

When my wife and I describe an incident to friends, I tend to start the story just before the climax; she backs way up to include details and color I can never remember anyway. Was my version inaccurate? Nope, just incomplete.

Verbal communication is by nature subjective and misleading. This is because spoken words aren't as complete as our thoughts. Our brains filter everything we say and hear to accommodate our thought patterns. We may reveal part of what we're thinking, or someone may process what we say with meanings we never intended.

This sort of nuanced communication contrasts the black-and-white world of truth and lies. It's the shades of gray that trip us up the most in our own conversations.

Have you ever heard these words?

> "That's not what I meant!"
> "You never listen to me."
> "You always read into what I say!"
> "I just don't get you."

In these situations, it's not that someone necessarily lies. You approach the discussion from your angle while they come from theirs.

If our boss tells us both we did a good job, you might thank him and feel motivated to do even better; I might pick apart his choice of words or evaluate his tone and conclude he really wants to fire me.

It's like we all have blinders on. Or perhaps more accurately, it's like we're wearing colored glasses. Our points of view are shaded by our personalities, ambitions, fears, and experiences.

Whatever your hue is, I believe Henry Ford was spot on. The secret of success lies in seeing through other people's eyes—putting on their glasses. To lead successfully, we must see the entire spectrum reflecting all around us, which means taking off our own spectacles first.

This book is about a leader who learns this truth the hard way. Leo Perkins, a confident CEO, is blind to anyone's view but his own. He casts a turnaround vision for his company and invites people to buy in, but their reactions shock him. His team's doubts and fears manifest in strange ways. Ultimately, he must make a dramatic decision about his—and his company's—future.

Philo's famous admonition to "be kind, for everyone you meet is fighting a great battle" succinctly summarizes the message of *Through Colored Glasses*. Leo falls victim to a dozen internal battles he never realizes are being waged. They come to a head even as he makes his do-or-die presentation in the climax of the book.

How do leaders deal with these unspoken tensions?

The Bible says, "The purposes of a person's heart are deep waters, but one who has insight draws them out" (Prov. 20:5).

Jesus had this insight. He saw into people's hearts as the Holy Spirit revealed their thoughts and attitudes to him. He understood their battles.

At the end of the book, we'll look at some biblical wisdom and exciting scriptural truths that open up people's hearts to us in the same way.

I promise your leadership—and your life—will be transformed.

Now on to the battle.

PART 1

Nothing is so painful to the human mind as a great and sudden change.
—Mary Shelley, writer

When Leo Perkins retrieved his buzzing phone and saw the name of the caller, his drowsy eyes blinked twice. The ocean breeze suddenly lost its sweetness and the hot sand intensified under his feet.

He felt his wife's gaze as she adjusted her sunglasses. As much as he had tried to master his facial expressions, he couldn't hide stress from Teresa.

"Is it him?" Her eyebrows tightened just over the rims of her dark lenses. "Now?"

"Yep." Leo shook his head and sighed. So much for this oasis away from the job. He pressed "accept" and sank into the lounge chair.

Teresa pointed at the phone, whispering like a muted steam engine. "Well, you can just tell that man to—"

Leo pushed his palm toward her. "This is Leo. Yeah, how are you, Bill?"

Despite his seven decades, the caller's whiny voice sounded like a college kid's. But Bill Grafton made up for his stature with practiced curtness. "Are you still flying through Miami tomorrow? We need to meet. Things are heading sideways. We've got to make some changes."

Heading sideways? Changes? Where did this come from? Last he knew, Leo was still the golden boy in the eyes of the board. He'd righted the ship by putting some new hands on deck and single-handedly landing the largest account in company history.

The only other time the chairman had placed this kind of impromptu call was to offer Leo the CEO's job a few years ago. The fact that he was calling after so long—while Leo and his wife were on vacation, no less—meant there was about to be blood in the water.

Leo's mind sharpened as adrenaline lit him up. He was going to have to speed up his plans and unfold his new vision *now*.

"Can I call you later this afternoon?" Leo couldn't look at Teresa. Her slamming down her piña colada voiced her protest. "Or when we get home tomorrow night?"

"What time will you be landing in Miami tomorrow?" Bill asked. "Still 3:20? I'll swing by the airport."

There was no escape. When the chairman of Carter Phillips called a meeting, you took it. Even if you were on your first vacation in three years.

Leo smiled his politician's smile to force confidence into his voice. "Yep, 3:20. It'll be great to see you. Keep in mind we've only got a ninety-minute layover."

"This won't take long. Come out to baggage claim and someone will be waiting there. We'll meet in my car." The phone went silent. Leo's smile hung lifeless.

He was determined to not let this meeting be his last.

Before dinner, while Teresa was in the shower, Leo called Will Freeman.

As his publisher, Will was Leo's rainmaker—full of youthful energy, ambition, and creativity. His relative newness to the job was overshadowed by experience at Riverton Business Media, one of the largest publishers in the country. Leo needed every ounce of this young man's bravado, political savvy, and killer instinct.

But he needed it fast, before his wife emerged from the bathroom and caught him working again. The call from Bill had ruthlessly invaded her privacy, breaking Leo's promise of a no-work week in the sun with full attention focused on her. The Bahamas had been perfect. Right up until that call. He had a lot of making up to do—especially since he was going to desert her tomorrow.

Will answered with a huffed breath. "Yes, sir?"

"Will, sorry to bother you this late, but we've got a situation."

"Sure thing, Leo. Let me hop off this thing so I can focus." The steady background noise deadened.

"You still work out twice a day?" Leo asked. "Making me look bad."

"Nah, just keeping up with the boss. How can I help?"

"I just got a call from Bill Grafton."

"Whoa, that can't be good. Aren't you still at the beach?"

"Yeah. He wants to meet me at the airport tomorrow afternoon on our way home. There's going to be stuff hitting the fan at this meeting, I'm sure. I know this is short notice, but I need that presentation you've been working on."

"You mean Vision One? But it's still pretty rough. We haven't finished talking about the restructuring part."

"I know." Teresa turned off the water. Leo paused and stepped out onto the porch. "Look, I just need him to understand we've got a plan and we know what we're doing."

I need him to realize he can't fire me.

"I understand." Will's voice hardened. "I won't let you down, sir. I'll fire off something to you in the morning."

∞

Leo decided to risk a second call—just a quick one. Hal Perrone didn't talk much, anyway. As CFOs went, he fit the mold: conservative, emotionless, regimented, precise, impatient. Of course, being a former Marine accentuated those qualities, adding intensity and discipline to the mix.

Leo felt little love for the man. Maybe it was because he outranked Leo in age as well as tenure, and he constantly found ways to remind everyone of his seniority. As one of few survivors from the old regime, Hal bore his scars like a badge of courage. He actually strutted through the halls. *Surely he knew how many people didn't like him?*

Right now, Hal's likability was the least of Leo's concerns. He needed the man's financial prowess. He also planned on leveraging Hal's relationship with Bill and others on the board. They'd kept him after the last regime change for a reason.

After a few rings, Hal's voice came across faintly. "Yes, Leo?"

"I hate to bother you, but I really need your help."

"I heard you talked to Bill."

"Right. Look, Hal, I'm in a situation here. My Vision One plan needs to be fast-tracked."

"Okay."

"Can you have the numbers to me by noon tomorrow?"

The pause heightened Leo's blood pressure. "I suppose I could have an abbreviated version," Hal finally said.

"Great. I need a revised pro forma for year one, historical company performance for the past four years, and then one more thing." Leo bit his lip. "I need you to call the bank and expedite the renewal on our line of credit. If you can, add another few hundred grand to it."

"Are you serious?"

"I'm afraid I couldn't be more serious. You're the one who told me cash isn't looking good. I need every stop pulled out before my meeting with Bill." Leo sighed. "I think you know what this kind of meeting has to be about."

"I'll see what I can do."

Will Freeman snarled at the fact that Leo's project had interrupted his regular morning workout. To make up for the lost time and unburned calories, he promised himself he'd double the intensity on the treadmill that evening.

By way of a group text he'd summoned his entire team for this 6:30 a.m. meeting. Though he'd worked on the presentation himself until 2 o'clock in the morning, pieces of it still eluded him, and his concept for additional graphics needed his team's polish.

Panic never overtook him, but it sure nipped at his heels this morning. He needed to stay a step ahead of it and project confidence.

He pushed through the conference room door. "Thanks for coming in. If you haven't had your coffee, I brought the strong stuff." He dropped a box of cups brimming with dark roast on the table.

Their groggy expressions aimed at the brew. Once they filled up and settled back down, Will said, "Sorry to drag you out of bed. But our CEO may lose his job if we don't help him out. I need you to be sharp and highly caffeinated for the next several hours. Everything else is on hold. We need to hone Vision One to perfection so Leo can present it to Carter Phillips this afternoon."

Everyone was awake now.

"It's not just Leo's job on the line," Will said. "It's ours, too. I'm getting wind of another housecleaning in the works."

Leo found himself holding his breath and then gasping for air as he half-jogged past the gates. Hundreds of people, each with their own uncomfortable expressions, sat or moved throughout the massive Miami terminal.

He tried not to sweat, which required a slower pace. But he only had a few minutes to get to baggage claim. How many stinking gates and concourses could there be?

Leo willed himself to breathe and slow his steps. He should be more confident than this. At forty-four, he was in his prime: healthy, strong, and still athletic even though college baseball sat more than twenty years behind him. He had reached the pinnacle of his career; any company would be lucky to pick him up if he left Industrial.

But the thought of leaving—especially being fired—horrified him. The embarrassment would kill him.

Why did Bill hold so much sway over him? He was one of few people in the world who intimidated Leo. Maybe the Purple Heart from Vietnam did it, or his family's millions. It could simply be that icepick stare. Or the fact that he stood a foot taller than Leo.

And so what if the Industrial turnaround had stalled? Every company had its cycles. This downturn was temporary, a minor blip soon to be forgotten once Vision One took off.

Leo checked his phone one more time. The presentation from Will had arrived just as he and Teresa had positioned themselves at the bar in the lounge. Hal had sent the numbers an hour earlier, with everything he'd asked for. "No word on the LOC" came back as the only response to Leo's request to expand the line of credit with the bank. Just like Hal to leave him hanging.

Leo finally saw the baggage sign with an arrow slanting down. He was going to make it. When he reached the bottom of the escalator, he spotted a dark-suited young man holding the "Carter Phillips" sign. They locked eyes and with a cold nod, the man led Leo out of the terminal. *Like boss, like chauffeur.*

8

They approached a stretch limo waiting at the curb in the stifling Miami air. At least Bill respected him enough to come first class. The young man opened the door, beckoning Leo to enter the dark interior.

Bill Grafton was not smiling. Nor were the three other board members sitting next to him.

For a moment Leo's brain sent nothing to his mouth. His thoughts stuck in the back of his throat. He stared at the group as a whole rather than individual faces.

"Hello, Leo." Bill's smug voice brought Leo to his senses.

"This is a surprise," Leo said, trying to smile. "I mean, well, a pleasure."

Bill's face came into focus. He was wearing a suit, as were his companions. "You know Bonita Carter, founding director of CP. She flew in from Toronto. To her left is Sam Phillips Jr., son of our other founding director. On the end is someone you haven't met. Christopher Hilton." Bill added no qualifier after his name. Leo restrained the question—but obviously this guy was going to be his replacement.

"Thank you for meeting with us," Bill continued. The others stared silently. "Let me get right to it. Yesterday the four of us were having an impromptu executive committee meeting at my flat downtown. We do this once or twice a year to talk about things. It came up that Industrial Publications just completed its second full year of turnaround."

"In a three-year plan," Leo said.

"Nevertheless, the company's results this far into your plan are dismal and heading for disaster."

"Excuse me, Bill—can you clarify what you mean by 'disaster?'" Leo's heart picked up speed again. This was going dark way too fast. "Before you give me your verdict, can I at least make my case and present a new plan?"

"You mean you've revised year three of the original plan?" Sam asked. "Aren't you a little late for that?" His curly hair seemed at odds with his suit. The young man looked like he'd been plucked from Miami Beach.

Leo clenched his jaw. "No," he said. "An entirely new plan. I call it Vision One."

"By 'disaster,' I mean a trend downward with an obvious ending," Bill said. "Revenue, expenses, cash on hand, and receivables are past the point of no return. A new vision is a waste of time. The old one wasn't executed."

Leo had to get control. But Bonita cut in. "We already bought into your last plan. It didn't work. Now you want us to listen to you again? We don't have any more time or money for that."

"Wait, wait a minute," Leo said, raising his palms. "The market has changed. We have new competitors. New technology is disrupting the industries we cover—not just disrupting, but decimating them. Granted, we have some people that need to be replaced. Plus, we've never had enough of a cash cushion to make me comfortable. But remember that I've in fact grown revenue by 15 percent over the past two years and stemmed the tide of losses caused by my predecessor."

Leo rushed ahead so none of them could interrupt. "I'm not sure what financials you're looking at, but this business is not about to die. Give me ten minutes to explain my new strategy. It's drastic enough to get your attention, believe me."

Christopher, whoever he was, narrowed his eyes slightly. Leo could see each of his opponents clearly now and felt more confident. "I know you have doubts. But you have no idea what I'm going to present, do you?"

Sam harrumphed. Bonita raised one eyebrow. Bill turned his head askew but kept his eyes frozen. "I didn't bring you out here to lecture us on your version of reality," he said. "We are intimate with CP's businesses and know when changes need to be made in one of them."

"That's why you want to hear what I'm proposing." Leo leaned in, capturing Bill's gaze in his own. "I guarantee my changes will be effective. There will be a complete turn-around in six months, or I will resign. No questions asked."

"Give us what you've got," Bill said. His arms folded as if he'd just dropped a gauntlet.

That's more like it. Leo yanked his phone out and began the presentation of his life.

PART 2

If you're paralyzed with fear, it's a good sign.
It shows you what you have to do.

—Steven Pressfield

Leo studied the familiar slides on his screen. They lacked the excitement they'd delivered in the limo. Maybe he was just tired. Leo swigged a hot sip from his carafe, hoping to manufacture the edge he'd need for the management meeting in an hour. He craved approval from his team. Surely they'd get behind it as he delivered it.

He still wondered what the limo group thought about Vision One. Only Bonita had hinted at her approval. Bill's dubious squints gave him a little more to work with than the flat frown from Christopher Hilton. Maybe the guy was just too busy devising his plan to steal Leo's ideas down the road. Sam's disapproval had been obvious and expected.

The truth was Leo Perkins needed more than strong coffee and a good meeting to turn this company around. The weight of a potentially nonexistent future had descended like a shroud inside that limo.

This morning it started seeping into his soul.

You can make it. Susan Haversham had recited this mantra every morning for God knew how many years. First, she made it through her divorce and the ensuing loneliness. Then her daughter left. Then financial ruin overtook her. Then, of course, the stress of it all had built up in her body over the years. At sixty-seven, she was afraid her health would collapse any day.

Her joints fought her this morning as she got out of the car. While the long, painful walk to the building often soured her for the whole day, today she had to move faster despite the aches. Leo needed help before the meeting. He had been there for her the past few years. She'd never forget his generosity with giving her extra time off and paying one of her doctor bills. This was the least she could do.

"Susan! Wait up." Patrick Kwon bounded out of his car and jogged a few steps. "Can I carry that?"

She smiled. This young man could've been her friend if he was about thirty years older. His awkwardness and lack of athleticism drew her motherly instincts. "You sure can." She handed him the doughnuts. "Leo's got a tough day ahead of him."

"Do you know what this meeting's about?"

"The HR VP knows what *all* meetings are about." She stifled her pain and donned a pleasant face. "And today is going to be a doozy."

Patrick studied the cement as he walked. This poor boy didn't know what to do with her. She wanted to prepare him to hear the hard news, but she also didn't want to be the one to scare him.

That was Leo's job.

Patrick dropped the doughnuts off in the kitchen but not without snatching one. A snack here and there wouldn't hurt.

Poor Susan. She reminded him of his mom: gentle, non-tech, vulnerable. Out of her element in this fast-moving business. How would she handle all the stress thrown at her today? She always seemed on the verge of some kind of emotion—mostly sadness.

Though he felt a twinge of trepidation himself about the meeting, as CTO he enjoyed a certain level of job security. But if the company were at risk, of course, life would change for him. Drastically.

Losing his job would ruin everything—how was a man supposed to propose to his girlfriend if he had no job? The shame would scare off the first girl that had ever taken an interest in him.

"Hello, Patrick." He nearly dropped the remaining half of his doughnut. Hal Perrone stood in the shadows at the coffeemaker. "Ready for the meeting?"

"Well, sure," Patrick said. This guy's Marine-ness always rubbed people way wrong. "I've got a few things to do beforehand, but—"

"I'm sure you do. Are you ready for the worst?"

Patrick clamped down on his tongue. He'd love to tell this guy off. Maybe he should do it in Korean and finally let out the steam that had built up for so long.

"If it goes bad, stick with me, kid." As Hal strode out of the kitchen, his gaze struck Patrick as odd.

Chief Marketing Officer Linda Durbin arrived at her usual 8:15 a.m. starting time. She parked in her usual spot, said hi to the usual people on the way in, and grabbed her coffee. Patrick ducked out of the kitchen without returning her greeting.

No matter. This was going to be a good day. The meeting was finally here. She'd sensed the displeasure of the bosses at HQ for several months now. Her analysis of Industrial's latest audience outreach campaign revealed an apathy the board had reflected in the last quarterly call.

It was truth time. Leo had avoided it as long as possible. Poor guy. Ever since he'd assumed the CEO post a few years ago, he'd meant well, but key people just wouldn't accept him. She'd tried to talk Hal into giving up his loyalty to the old CEO, but he was so cold and his grudges ran deep. There was no love lost between him and . . . well, anyone.

Linda loved truth. Today she knew she'd hear it, but she also prepared her heart for the usual politicking, greed, and selfish ambition rampant in IP's management meetings.

And if she lost her job? She reminded herself that her calling wouldn't change; she'd just shine somewhere else. God had provided for her and her husband generously for many years. She would serve her Lord wherever he led.

As she turned the corner near her office, Will Freeman walked out of his.

"Hey, early bird," she said.

Will nodded and kept walking. She followed him and stopped in his doorway. "Need anything before the meeting?"

"No, the design team has given me everything I need," he said without looking up from his phone. She waited politely for an acknowledgment of her help on Leo's presentation.

He wasn't biting. "You excited about today?" she asked.

He looked up with intense, tired eyes. "Is there any-thing I can help you with?"

Linda smiled and backed away from the door. "See you in an hour, Will."

Will Freeman tried to process the numbers Hal had just sent him. Not only would he have to change the spread-sheet and the slides at the last minute, but Leo was going to have a stroke.

Did Hal *want* the company to fail? These "revised" numbers made Leo out to be a liar. He had promised growth; this spreadsheet delivered losses. What kind of CFO undercut his boss like this?

One determined to win at any cost. One who was disloyal and had close ties with the parent company. No wonder he always seemed nonchalant about his work—there was no threat to his job. It was obvious he wanted Leo out.

But Leo had hired Will, giving him a chance to build something great and jumpstart his own career. He was finally putting his MBA to good use. Anything that jeopar-dized this job—at least until he added another couple years to his resume—was a personal threat.

Hal Perrone was formidable but not invincible. If Will wanted to succeed here, Leo and his plan must succeed. If they canned Leo, Will wouldn't be far behind. And what would that do to his career prospects? No one in Manhattan would hire him.

All those thousand-dollar suits would just keep on hanging in his closet.

Hal felt the corner of his mouth turn upward. *Fire in the hole.* He wished he could see Will's face upon reading the email.

A little stress was good for people. It created action, which this company needed. Leo was a good guy, but he would do everyone and himself a favor if he moved on. Leo would eventually find another job. Probably even a better one. In fact, Hal would help him by deferring blame for the downturn on others in the company.

Once Leo headed for the door, Hal would swoop back in with his own save-the-day strategy. He was the only one who could find immediate profit with his creative depreciation plan. Sure, there would be other casualties beyond Leo, but the company's future hinged on this move.

Will would be an ideal scapegoat for Industrial's demise. Leo had hired him, and Hal could claim Leo made a bad choice. The young man's big-city, holier-than-you attitude may have generated some short-term sales, but the projected downturn proved his tactics were lacking. Plus, his chauvinism and womanizing were causing too much turnover.

Yes, Will would take the hit for his boss and allow Leo a soft landing at another media company. Even Will would probably land on his feet. *But not with any help from me.*

"An emergency meeting?" Leo asked. "Right now? About what?"

Will knew it was a long shot thirty minutes before the management meeting. "Leo, I'd like to bring Susan with me to talk about something. It's about Hal. We need to talk now."

"What about him?"

"I just got some new numbers from him. Forwarded them to you. Did you get my email?"

"Not yet." Leo sounded pained. "All the numbers are in. There can't be anything new—he gave me his final revision yesterday."

"Hal's projections show a loss for the year. Leo, I think he's got an agenda."

"Not possible. Get in here."

Susan had an idea why Will was dragging her to see the CEO. He walked ahead of her down the long hall to Leo's suite. He pulled away from her with every step, oblivious to her pace. *So much for the common courtesy of waiting for a lady.*

Will had revealed only one thing to her about this "meeting before the meeting"—that it was life-and-death for the company and probably for Leo, too.

In the last great purging of the management team, only Linda and Hal had survived. And of course he continued to enjoy favor from corporate. Was Hal doing it again, orchestrating the demise of his peers in order to personally benefit? He'd certainly succeeded last time.

But not poor Leo, not now! He was so kind to her, supportive when others dismissed her as old school. She counted him among her short list of friends.

Not Leo.

"Come in, Susan, come in." Leo was grateful for the friendly face, if only for a moment. "Will was just about to drop the bomb."

"The bomb," Will said, "is Hal. He is about to sabotage your new strategy. He waited until just before the meeting to send us into a panic. Why didn't we see these numbers before now?"

"Okay, slow down," Leo said. "I've only perused his spreadsheet, but it doesn't look like the end of the world."

"He's not only recast history and ratcheted down your projections, he's shot holes in your credibility in plain view of corporate. Did you notice he cc'd Bill Grafton on the e-mail to me? He didn't even include you in the send." Will sat down. Leo sank with him.

"I'll contain it in the meeting," Leo said. "I'll tell him his numbers need more vetting, and that he can't just drop these on me without warning."

"Sir, if I may, you'll need to be a little stronger than that," Susan said. "Will's right. I've seen this kind of thing before. You've got to unfortunately come out swinging. You need to address these revised numbers head on—somehow. I'll be behind you as best I can."

Leo spun his chair to face the window. He needed time to think. He always got himself out of corners like this. But never had he felt pressure from so many directions.

His desk phone came alive with his assistant's voice. "Sir, I've got a call for you."

"Not now, Emily. Really, not now."

"I'm sorry, but he insisted."

Leo swung back to his desk. "Who is it?"

"Bill Grafton."

Of course. "Can you tell him I'll call him after the meeting? I've got a situation here that needs every bit of my attention before it starts in thirty minutes."

Emily's silence hung for a moment. "He really wants to talk to you, Leo. I already tried to delay. He said it's *about* the meeting."

Leo clenched his jaw. What could possibly be so urgent? Grafton already knew every word Leo was going to tell his staff. "Send him through."

"Yes sir."

Leo punched the speaker phone button. "Hi, Bill. Good to hear from you. What can I do for you?"

"I know you've got a meeting with your management team later this morning," Bill said. "This will just take a second."

"No worries. Your call's welcome anytime."

"Do you have a conferencing capability?"

"I'm sorry?"

"I want someone to patch into the meeting. On the phone is fine. He won't participate, just listen."

"May I ask who?"

"Of course. Christopher Hilton."

Leo stifled the curses building up on his tongue. The battle with Hal was enough.

"Like I said," Bill continued, "he's just going to listen. You won't even know he's there. He just wants to learn more about the operation."

"May I ask why?"

"We're retaining him as a consultant."

Leo heard Bill's words, but his mind refused to process them. Given the situation, the "consultant" term carried all kinds of meanings.

"Oh, and one other thing," Bill said. "There may be a few other management teams from some of our companies listening in. Again, they won't be asking questions or participating in any way. We'll do a roundtable soon for that."

Leo estimated his audience had just doubled. *You want me to go ahead and pack my things and get out?*

"Send me the dial-in and the time and that'll be that. Thanks, Leo."

After dismissing Will and Susan, Leo closed his door. The one thing he needed right now was silence. His mind needed to settle and recharge, even if just for a few minutes.

The numbers were what they were. Will said he'd grapple with them some more, but Leo held little hope he'd be able to defend Hal's attack. Leo's only idea was to defer the official release of his projections until after the meeting.

But he had two problems. First, he'd promised his team a complete Vision One. Without impressive financial goals at the heart of his strategy, where did that leave the rest of his plan? Any faint credibility he clung to would turn into mist without solid financials. He could try to discredit Hal somehow, but he knew that ship wouldn't sail with corporate defending him.

His second problem was the enigmatic Christopher Hilton. Mystery Man was now a spy. He represented the long arm of Carter Phillips preparing to choke Leo into submission. The way Hilton had stared at him, Leo knew resistance was futile.

Poor Teresa. She'd married an ambitious, daring, confident, dreamy-eyed loser. What should've been the apex of his career—of his very life—had devolved into defeat.

But this loser, he vowed, would go down shootin'.

Linda Durbin knew this wasn't the ideal time to knock on Leo's door. But, she told herself, it could be the most important conversation she'd ever had with him.

She stood before the imposing entrance, praying for confirmation that she was still supposed to do this. The fact that she had coasted right by Emily, who remained focused on a phone call, was confirmation enough. *No going back now.*

She watched her knuckle hit the wood. *Too loud*, she thought. Her second, softer tap sent more of the message she came to deliver: *I'm here as your friend.* She added a third knock. *But I'm not going away.*

"Excuse me," came the protest behind her. Emily was always so protective of her boss. "Oh, hi, Linda. It's you. Sorry. He asked me to give him a moment before the meeting. Can I get you some time with him this afternoon instead?"

Linda paused, hoping her knock had stirred Leo's curiosity. "Didn't mean to interrupt your call, Emily. Thanks for the offer. I think he's going to want to hear what I have to say. It's urgent."

"Before this meeting?" Emily asked. "Are you sure it can't wait?"

"It'll just take a minute. I've got a quick little encourager beforehand that he needs."

"Well, I'm not sure. . . ."

Suddenly the door opened. "What is it, Emily? I thought I told you . . ." Leo caught himself. "Linda? What's up?"

She smiled. He looked horrible.

"I hope you didn't come to heap more on me," he said retreating into his office. "I'm full up with everyone giving me their advice and drama."

Linda followed him in and closed the door. "I will do nothing of the sort, sir."

"Well, then, what've you got? I really don't have time."

"I'll get right to the point. Leo, you know I don't need to work. I don't need this job. My husband brings home plenty of bacon. You also know I'm one of two managers from the old regime, along with Hal. Everyone's aware he's giving you problems. So as the only other veteran here, I needed to give you some perspective on your meeting." She paused, unsure about the tense expression he projected. But she had to ignore it. "Two years ago, I knew God wanted me to stay at the company. Today he's shown me one of the reasons."

"Thanks, Linda, but I don't need a God lecture right now." Leo held his coffee mug to his mouth like a barrier between them.

"I understand. But he not only wanted me to stay at IP, he wanted me to come talk to you right now. I literally didn't know what I was supposed tell you—until right this very moment."

Leo's eyes softened, then he looked away.

"So here it is," she continued. "Sometimes leaders try to do everything right and are innocent of ulterior motives. Sometimes they succeed, sometimes they don't. At least, not right away. Sometimes they become a target for everyone's frustrations, a lightning rod of sorts. The thing is there's only so much you can control. A lot of us know this about you as our CEO, and they cut you slack. But there are others who don't even use slack when they *fish*."

She waited for a sign she should continue. He didn't smile, but he also remained silent. Sign enough. "There's a verse in Proverbs that I think will help you. It says, 'Like a fluttering sparrow or a darting swallow, an undeserved curse does not come to rest.' Leo, sometimes God wants us to trust him to hold back the tide. That's all I wanted to tell you. Ask God to keep the undeserved curse from falling on you."

His face softened more, but Linda didn't wait for a response. "Thanks for listening, Leo. I hope you draw some comfort from that. See you in a few minutes."

As she fled his office, she trusted she hadn't added to the drama he abhorred so much. She knew God's Word never came back void, but she wondered if she'd chosen the right Scripture and the right time.

She had no idea how the Lord would fulfill his promise from Proverbs. She felt somewhere deep inside, though, that he would surprise them all.

PART 3

The only way around is through.

—Robert Frost

He usually swooped into a meeting right at starting time, but today Leo arrived early. Linda's visit was still on his mind. If only her verse about the undeserved accusations and attacks were true.

At least he knew his attackers. Obviously, Carter Phillips as the parent had every right to oust the CEO of one of its underperforming companies. This happened in the business world every day. But the lies of Hal Perrone—and Bill Grafton's cold manipulation—implied more personal agendas.

The smell of Leo's blood in the water had surely invited Hal to strike, though he'd never concealed his desire for Leo's job over the past two years. While he could name the handful of times Hal had publicly resisted him, the CFO had never undermined him with such bold fabrications. Bill's aggression gave apparent blanket permission to Hal to heap on the pressure.

Leo filled up his super-tall carafe but drew only a sip. He'd downed so much java already this morning that his hands shook.

Will arrived first, striding in with his usual flash. Leo's spirits lifted slightly. This young man knew how to scrap his way out of impossible situations. The smile stretching over his tense jaw accentuated his red tie.

"I think I've got something that might help counteract Hal's numbers," Will said. "It's not a home run, but it could be enough to slow him up." He flipped open his tablet and swiped the screen. "I've worked on a quick personnel chart. If you restructured admin and circulation, you could—"

Leo lifted a hand. "Look, Will, I trust you." He glanced into the hallway. "But people are about to walk in. Whatever you've got I'm sure is good. Bring it up when you think it's appropriate. I don't question your loyalty or talent for a second. Let's just see how the meeting goes."

Will squinted, then nodded and slowly closed his tablet. "Right." He visibly composed himself. "We're going to be fine."

Leo touched his shoulder and moved past him to greet the shadows approaching the door.

"Thank you all again for coming," Leo said to the packed conference room. Someone tapped a pen on their coffee cup to get everyone quiet. A few friendly faces stood out; the other dozen registered fear or slightly shrouded disdain. He guessed another ten or twenty listened on the phone, though their relative friendliness remained in question.

"I hope everyone on the line can hear. If you have technical issues at any time, please text my assistant Emily and she'll get on it." He gave them her number.

"With so many people here today," he continued, "this will out of necessity be more of a presentation than a conversation, though there'll be time for Q&A at the end. Those of you who are remote can enter a question through chat at any time. I do have a slide deck today, which is viewable if you're logged in on our conference line. If you don't have a way to view it live, text Emily and she'll send it to you."

Leo paused to let everyone finish settling. He inhaled deeply. *Here we go.*

"Today is a big day. You all are considered the most senior people in Industrial Publications. I welcome this opportunity to share our new strategy—you deserve to know where we're going. But you also deserve to know where we are and how we got here. So let me give you a little background."

As he gathered the words of his next sentence, his tension lessened. This warm-up was the easy part.

"As you know, IP has been around over fifty years. That's much longer than most companies will ever make it. We've had such incredible staying power in large part because of the strong platform built by our founders, and most recently by our new parent, Carter Phillips. We've always hired the best and executed with excellence. We've been publishing in strong markets that themselves have been around for decades and will continue to grow and flourish."

Leo paused. He wanted to stay on this safe ground for as long as he could.

"We've made a few acquisitions over the years. We launched new magazines and events. We've won awards for great content and design. We've even turned down bids to buy our company. That is, until three years ago, when CP acquired us—the first time someone ever successfully bought us out. The leadership changes we went through were stressful for everyone, but we pushed through and today we're in position for a bright future.

"Of course, we've had our share of challenges the past few years—like the problems with modernizing our paper magazines to become digital, and the brave new world of building advanced content websites to stay competitive. It seems like everyone and their uncle became publishers when the Internet lowered the bar in this business.

"It's these challenges that have conspired to bring us to a new inflection point. We need to make changes and take risks, or our competition will lap us. On top of this, our magazines continue to decline in revenue. So we've got a double-whammy—we need to turn around our print fall-off while moving up on digital and events. If we keep going without doing these things, we'll hit a downward tipping point that will be hard to recover from."

Leo knew he came across negatively, but he prided himself on telling the truth. "Carter Phillips as a venture capital company would rightly question their investment if we kept going like we are. The numbers in our current projections are dismal. Cash is in a bad way, just when CP needs it to make another acquisition. Growth has left the building, which means the prospects of recovering any cash aren't rosy. Good people are starting to leave, too. Many of them said they didn't believe in our future.

"Well, I am here to announce our brand-new future. Something we can *all* believe in. Because if we keep going without a vision, we'll keep walking on our current path. All we're doing is managing decline—not pushing growth."

He caught Will's eye and gave him a half-wink. "Lest you think I'm inferring that the blame for our revenue and audience shortfalls should land on the shoulders of any single person here, rest assured that we all have a part to play in our success. We can't sell a single thing or attract a single reader unless our processes, design, website back end, customer service, accounting, and all our other departments are firing on all cylinders. And I'll add to the list that the CEO must be at the top of his game, too, supporting all of you. I know I can improve in this area."

Will's face lost its defensive edge and he nodded.

"Now I'd like to lay out my new vision for the company. I call it Vision One. I chose the name to stress the unity we've got to have, or else we have nothing. We must act like one body with many parts, rather than disjointed units pulling in different directions with different goals. I've been working on this new strategy for the past six months as I've taken a sharp look at IP's strengths and weaknesses. And believe me, we've got both—many of which you're aware of, some which might be a little less obvious.

"When Bill Grafton hired me three years ago, my job was to merge IP into CP, and use the synergies to take us higher. While it hasn't been easy, and the results have left all of us a little wanting, I'm proud and excited to introduce to you Vision One." Leo cued the young man on the slides, who dimmed the lights and brought up the presentation.

While people's eyes adjusted and focused on the screen, Leo assessed his executive team. Will was on board and ready to leap into the fray if things got ugly. Linda's ever-present smile reassured him, while Susan's customary drabness seemed extra gray this morning. Though Leo didn't know Patrick Kwon very well, the kid did nothing to hide his anxiety as he slumped over the edge of the table. Hal gave up nothing on his cold, combat-ready face.

"We'll accomplish three major goals that span the short and long terms," Leo said. "First, we will achieve 100 percent improvement in our top four metrics over the next four years. These key performance indicators include ad revenue, subscriber renewals, site traffic, and net profit. Second, we'll launch one new magazine and conference per year into the foreseeable future. Finally, we'll cut our debt by one-third and build our cash reserves for further investment."

"We're going to hit these goals by adopting a new philosophy and a new culture," Leo continued. "We must abandon the old ways that got us where we are. My new philosophy is simple: it's *growth*. This is the inspiration behind Vision One. We're going to have one thought in our minds every day when we come to work, one solution when we deal with issues, one driver of every meeting we're in. Our entire culture will be about one thing—growth!

"When you check your e-mail in the morning, I want you to ask yourself, 'How can I help the company grow today?' When you've got a problem of any sort, I want you to figure out a solution centered on growth—not just on more efficiency, or just going far enough to fix the problem at hand. When you go home at night or turn off the light in your home office, I want you to assess your day. Evaluate whether you grew as an employee. Did you improve in any way? Did you make progress toward skills development? Did you learn something? Did you make strategic plans for your personal improvement?

"If we all grow as people, and dedicate our days to growing this company, we will succeed in this vision. It's when we focus on problems, processes, and getting our own way that we'll slow down. We've got to keep moving forward, making progress out of problems, and skipping over incremental improvements to leapfrog into growth. Sure, we'll deal with some glaring problems, but if the whole ship has to slow down to move a log out of the way, I say run right over it!

"So, whenever there's doubt about what to do next, the answer is one thing: growth. No matter what presents itself to you, I want you to see only one thing: a growth opportunity. This is the heart of Vision One. Along with that, remember there's only one speed for us: furiously fast. One outcome: success. There is no excuse—not one— for falling short.

"This is my commitment to you and to Carter Phillips. This is what will turn the company around. This is Vision One."

Leo looked down. Adrenalized energy still throbbed through his mind. He waited for a response. Any kind of reinforcement would've been nice, but he accepted the silence nevertheless.

"Now I'd like to break out the budget and start getting tactical. You're going to see some numbers on this year's projected performance that leave a little to be desired, but you know I like to deal in truth. This is where we are, but it's far from where we're going, I promise." He turned to the screen behind him. "Please bring up the financials."

Leo sensed Hal leaning forward.

Will Freeman sat down as the meeting's participants took their positions. Somehow his boss kept up the front as he personally welcomed everyone entering the conference room.

Will's resolve to win was more powerful than his desire to be friendly. He knew some measure of anxiety registered on his face, but he didn't care.

The battleground took shape. Hal snuck in and took a seat right next to Leo's. *Always so strategic.* Everyone who looked at Leo would see Hal. The main-event fight would be front and center.

As the other seats filled up, the sound level rose. The rest of the management team took spots at the table, while their key team members sat against the wall. Two of Will's own people sat behind him. They knew not to bother him with small talk.

Susan, sitting directly across from Will, tried desperately to look supportive. All she managed was a pained grin. She was always nervous—now she just looked *scared.*

Leo walked to the head of the table, raised his hands, and extended his smile. "Thank you all again for coming," he said. Will helped him grab attention with a few taps on his coffee mug.

The rest of the preamble was generic enough. Nothing Will hadn't already heard and baked into the presentation deck. He watched the faces at the table. Linda smiled at Leo, as usual. Poor Patrick couldn't hide his fear. Hal projected his customary cold stare, though dividing his attentions between the conference room and his laptop.

". . . All we're doing is managing decline—we're not pushing growth." That caught Will's attention. Leo winked at him and continued: "Lest you think I'm inferring that the blame for our revenue and audience shortfalls should land on the shoulders of any single person here, rest assured that we all have a part to play."

Will appreciated the attempted blame deferral, but it still hurt. Who else had revenue and audience development in their job description besides him? Will nodded just so Leo would move on. While the CEO always meant well, his words often got away from him.

As he turned the corner and headed for the financials, Will tensed. Now the real meeting would begin.

Susan Haversham didn't like meetings, but this one topped them all—even the times she'd had to fire friends she'd worked with for years.

When a coffee cup clinked, her attention jumped to Leo. His smile looked fake. Maybe she saw through it because she knew what was going on behind it. He was doing his best to appear confident. Poor soul.

Seeing her friend up there fighting back the dread pained her. She knew what that was like. Impending disaster was impossible to cover up, even with the best attitude adjustments. Her own experiences had taught her this—no amount of willed positivity could undo to the cancer she'd lived with, on top of the divorce, on top of the empty heart and home that never filled back up again. Surviving those dark experiences had changed her out-look on life, and the hopelessness now creeped back into her heart.

The one man in this world who looked out for her was himself in need of protection. But she couldn't give it. She could only watch in despair.

She tuned into Leo's words when his smile faltered. "Growth has left the building, which means the prospects of recovering any cash aren't rosy," he said. How was that supposed to motivate anybody?

"Good people are starting to leave, too. Many of them said they didn't believe in our future." *Oh no.* He was admitting defeat before giving himself a chance to earn his audience's confidence.

Susan tuned back out. The empathy pain she felt for her leader drowned out everything he said from then on.

Patrick Kwon stared at the table while Leo spoke. People always thought he wasn't paying attention when he looked down, but he didn't care. This was how he concentrated. Eye contact derailed his thoughts.

Today, none of his thoughts remained on the rails. He barely processed Leo's words until he said, "It's when we focus on problems, processes, and getting our own way that we'll slow down. We've got to keep moving forward, making progress out of problems, skipping over incremental improvements to leapfrog into growth."

Patrick lifted his eyes from the table, fixating on Leo. So "fixing problems" had suddenly dropped on the company's priority list? In other words, Patrick's team wasn't valued?

Leo had just admitted publicly that the IT and project management functions could be outsourced, defunded, or further minimized in the company's eyes.

Patrick was all *about* problems, processes, and incremental improvements. This was his job. His passion. He was proud to tell his parents that he had such a crucial role in the company. His girlfriend respected him for it.

He listened in horror. Everything he'd worked for—everything he *was*—meant less than nothing. He had even contributed to the company's lack of growth.

At thirty-five, Patrick knew this was his last chance to win his future wife and finally start a family. If he lost it all and had to start over, he might as well resign himself to a lonely life. No one would look at this old, overweight, washed-up geek as husband material.

Linda Durbin was sad. Watching everyone file in with downcast eyes and cursory greetings felt stifling. How could Leo lift the shroud hanging over the room? He couldn't do it alone—of that she was sure.

But he tried. His smile seemed genuine enough, and his voice still held its lilt. Those were skills he had honed over many years of being a front man. But he pushed against a weight no man could move. She saw it in the slight droop of his eyes, the slump in his shoulders. His confidence seemed a tinge manufactured.

So she prayed for him. That he would feel God's presence. That he'd receive authentic encouragement, not just a temporary boost from the force of his own will. That hearts—especially Bill Grafton's—would soften to his message. That he'd remember the verse from Proverbs.

She also prayed for Leo's salvation. She knew he'd survive this day, whether he kept his job or not. He would go on to lead a new vision, whether it was Vision One or another dream at another company. He was the type who would land on his feet. Life worked out for people like Leo Perkins.

But then there was eternity, *real* life. She wanted him to stay until *that* strategic plan worked out. If he left today, or if she herself became a corporate casualty, she'd lose the opportunity to share the gospel with him.

As he progressed through his opening talk, Linda's sadness subsided. God controlled the day, no matter what happened. She flowed with Leo's narrative, nodding and smiling at what she hoped were appropriate points. Truth was hard and he dealt it out with sensitivity. He needed a friendly face, not another detractor or critic.

When Leo allowed a moment of vulnerability, she smiled. His voice lost its artificial edge, if only for a moment. "And I'll add to the list that the CEO must be at the top of his game, too, supporting all of you," he said. "I know I can improve in this area."

In those few vulnerable sentences, his leadership grew. Here was a man she could follow. But she heard more from him than just hope for the company's future.

She sensed hope for his soul.

∞

Hal Perrone knew people watched him, but he had work to do. Now was the perfect time to give the spreadsheet the final spit-shine it needed.

He let the rest of the staff wonder what he was typing into his laptop. He didn't mind the added bonus of slightly distracting Leo as he tried desperately to rally these demoralized troops. The poor guy had no idea how his negativity only dug his grave deeper. Comments like "these challenges that have conspired to bring us to a new inflection point" and "we need to make changes and take risks, or our competition will lap us" only played into Hal's hand.

When Leo mentioned the continuing decline of magazine revenue, Hal chuckled. Exactly what he wanted to hear. This was going to be quick and painless—the best outcome for all concerned, especially Leo. No sense in garnering sore feelings from those Hal decided to keep on his team.

The speech continued: "We need to turn around our print fall-off while moving up on digital and events. If we keep going without doing these things, we'll hit a downward tipping point that will be hard to recover from."

Was it really going to be this easy? So many points of egress presented themselves that he wondered about his opponent's state of mind. Desperate men tended to lose the capacity for rational thought.

Hal let him go on while he worked on his spreadsheet. A few more tweaks of the depreciation line, sales compensation, and various expense projections would render the current year a loss, dimming the lights on Vision One for the next several years.

All the hype Leo worked so hard to generate would be swallowed up by facts and numbers. They cut through smoke and dreams with the knife of reality.

Hal's other strategic move had already played out perfectly. Bill had accepted his invitation to jump on the call after Hal simply requested that he compare Leo's strategy to his own.

Leo continued: "Carter Phillips as a venture capital company would rightly question their investment if we kept going like we are." Hal looked up from his laptop. "The numbers in our current projections are dismal. Cash is in a bad way, just when CP needs it to make another acquisition. Growth has left the building, which means the prospects of recovering any cash aren't rosy."

For a moment, Hal wondered if Leo knew what was coming. *Not possible.* Hal doubled his pace on the spreadsheet. He started working on his story, noting Leo's comments and crafting responses.

By the time Leo said, "Please bring up the financials," Hal had finished his work and e-mailed the file to one of his assistants sitting behind him, who instantly saved it to a thumb drive and walked it back to the guy running the A/V.

The plan rolled smoothly forward. *Time to gear up.*

PART 4

Either life entails courage, or it ceases to be life.

—E. M. Forster

Leo watched the exchange at the A/V booth between Hal's staffer and the tech. The quick chat and handoff of some item all happened in a matter of seconds. The young man glanced at Leo and then down at his equipment.

Though Leo had expected it, seeing Hal's altered numbers on the screen still jolted him.

He couldn't let this setback throw him off. "Before we get into the numbers themselves, let me give you a little more background," Leo said. "Recently we've been reviewing the projections for this year, and as each month has passed, we've ruthlessly reassessed where we think we'll be by the end of the year.

"What you're about to see is the latest version, with Hal's up-to-the-minute thinking. I've tasked him with keeping this projection as current as possible, so there are a few numbers that will likely be new to me, too." Leo nodded with a tight-lipped smile toward his CFO, letting people wonder whether it was out of appreciation or blame. "As we go through the highlights, I'm going to move pretty fast, since it'll change several more times before our year-end review. The bottom line is that this report is far from final."

That seemed to take some of the steam out of Hal's end run. He kept staring at his laptop.

"What I *can* tell you is that we're off our bottom-line budget by about 20 percent," Leo continued. "Revenue is flat and expenses are up. We hadn't anticipated some of the increased expenses from key employee departures, nor some of the resulting revenue loss. Some of their jobs were directly tied to revenue generation, so we experienced a greater setback as a result."

Leo decided to sidestep Hal's sabotage altogether. Who knew how many follow-up slides he'd slipped into the deck? "I tell you what. Since we're here today to focus more on the future than the past, we'll come back to the historical financial reports after the break. Deal?"

"Are you sure we can't go through it now?" Hal asked. "I'm sure some of us here would like to do a little more review of not just this year, but the past few."

The silence mushroomed. Leo tried to recover his confidence with a subtle smile. Everyone looked at Hal.

"Of course," Leo said. "I've got a historical review baked into the projections we're about to see. We'll also look at trends into the future so we get a proper perspective. Everyone okay with that?" He nodded at the A/V tech. "Let's roll back to my original presentation and keep going."

No one else except Leo could see Hal's eyes thin.

As the first slide appeared on the screen, Leo decided to ignore his nemesis. This was *his* meeting.

At least for the moment.

As Leo and Hal started trading blows, Susan wanted to flee right out that door. Her face felt hot. She had to remember to breathe. Her body felt heavy against the chair.

Short of running from the room, she retreated into her own thoughts.

But they weren't good thoughts. They consisted of the other tensions in her life: the loneliness she felt from the recent death of her beloved dog, the emptiness in her heart since her daughter's marriage and subsequent departure. Her own husband's exit twenty years ago also flooded back into her mind. She had never really recovered from the intense sense of desertion or the painful cancer she'd suffered.

Was Leo *about to leave now?*

As she settled into the thought of giving up, Susan's mind drifted to a faint tendril of hope: retirement. But now even that longing felt like an impossible dream. Not just because she couldn't afford it, but because this place had become a prison.

A prison in which the warden was about to be ousted by the ring-leader inmate.

As Will listened, his mind screamed at him to jump into the fight. His legs twitched as he leaned forward.

Allowing Hal's insubordinate interruption to go unanswered would cement his position. But, of course, if Will added to the disruption, he would appear rebellious as well. Which would not help Leo's attempt to regain control.

So, for the moment, he let the CEO navigate on his own. Will's steam nevertheless continued to rise.

"Let's roll back to my original projections and see where we're going." *Nicely done.* Leo re-gripped the steering wheel with that one, but overall his redirects only degraded his authority. Without hitting Hal hard, escalation was inevitable—the CFO's allies would get the knockout fight they wanted.

He saw Leo and Hal lock eyes. A cold silence hung between them until a new frame lit up on the screen. The diversion seemed to give permission to Leo to avert his attention back to the audience. As he geared up to speak, though, a slight sigh escaped his lips. Will wondered if anyone else heard it.

He vowed that the next time Hal took a swipe, it would be answered in kind. Leo was too nice.

Though he saw a tinge of anger on Will's face and felt his own temperature rising, Leo controlled his urge to lash out at Hal. With Bill and who knew who else on the conference line, not to mention all the company's top management in the room, not only would such a confrontation be embarrassing and inappropriate, it would jeopardize Leo's strategy.

But the dam would burst unless someone stepped up to help.

He looked at the screen once more, then forced a grin at the audience. "So here we go. Many of you have seen these spreadsheets before, or some previous draft of them. Remember, by definition, projections change all the time based on new information and circumstances. What I'm showing you is my best guess as to where we'll end up for the year. I'll also show you some history so we can understand the new strategy more fully."

Leo explained the relative performance of the company's main product lines, additional revenue sources, expenses, competitive pressures, the state of the market, progress on a defamation lawsuit, new product introductions, planned website innovations, and the company's cash reserve level. He carefully wove in historical trends without camping on the negative drivers.

He dove into taxes, donations, distributions, depreciation, legal fees, travel, and bad debt. He overwhelmed them with detail. *I know this company*, he was saying. *No one knows it better than I do. No one knows how to fix it better than I do.*

At least they remained attentive—a few nods here and there, a few narrowed gazes. He kept moving, driving home the heart of his message, barely pausing to breathe.

Hal stared with folded arms. Leo ignored the unmasked disdain and unpacked his strategy with every ounce of persuasion in his body.

Fifteen minutes later, he had made his case. From here on, there would be questions, feedback, comments of all sorts. Leo was ready. "Let's take a minute to turn off the projector and get a top-off on our coffee. Then we'll get your thoughts and questions."

He saw Hal tighten the fold of his arms.

As everyone broke for the coffee station, Linda ran up to Leo. She offered him her most encouraging smile.

"I know you really don't have time to chat," she said. "I just wanted to tell you you're doing a great job. You deflected him well."

"Thanks, Linda. But I'm afraid it's about to get worse. It's been easy so far."

"Everyone knows Hal's going to press his point. It's what he does. There's nothing you can do to prevent it. But when he gets rolling and you feel cornered, remember to trust God. He hears your thoughts and he can help."

She tapped his shoulder and backed away. She was proud of Leo's self-control and poise today.

But she knew he could teeter off the edge at any moment.

"How're you feeling about it so far?" Will asked.

"I'm not sure," Leo said. "Everyone's so quiet. Our friend seems like the only one interested in what I have to say."

"You handled him pretty well," Will whispered. "But is there any way you could be a bit stronger? I'm afraid people are getting the wrong message about your leadership."

"What message is that?"

"People know you as a nice guy. Smart. Willing to take risks." Will checked for eavesdroppers. "But to be honest with you, I wish you'd be a little less nice and take more risks standing up to Hal. You know he's gearing up for the next round. I'll follow your lead and am ready to tussle a bit."

"I appreciate that, but you don't have to—"

"Leo, I've got a strange feeling he's got some other surprise attacks coming. We need to preempt him."

"How?"

People started reclaiming their seats. Will raised his voice as the volume raised a couple notches. "Just go with your gut."

Patrick stood behind Susan in the coffee line. He thought she looked even more frail than earlier this morning. Surely she knew how forlorn she looked to people, with that pained expression she always carried.

She needed to get away from all the stress and let the younger people deal with it. She could collect her retirement income and just do what she wanted all day. Sleep in, watch movies, not feel rushed or pressured by anything or anyone.

Sounds good to me, Patrick mused.

Hal suddenly appeared on his left elbow, nearly touching him. "Pretty interesting, huh?"

"What's that?" Patrick asked. He immediately swiveled his head back to the front after glancing across Hal's eyes.

Susan didn't turn around, though Hal's voice seemed to startle her.

"The meeting so far." Hal sounded unusually self-satisfied. "Don't you think?"

"I'm not really sure what to think right now."

"Just remember what I told you this morning. Stick with me and I can guarantee you'll keep your job."

"Guarantee?" The word escaped Patrick's mouth.

Hal smiled but showed no teeth. Patrick regretted his response. But how in the world could anyone guarantee he would have a job after this?

Hal moved away just as Susan glanced back. She must've wondered the same thing.

"Okay, everyone," Leo said with a clap of his hands. He rubbed them together. "It's time to hear what you're thinking. You've heard me speak long enough. Give me your thoughts, questions, and comments."

Leo tensed as no one spoke up. A few stragglers were still settling, but for the most part people just looked at him. Will peered left and right and then back at Leo, almost as if seeking permission to say something. Leo narrowed his eyes, giving his compatriot a slight shake of the head. *Not yet.*

"I've got a question," Bill Grafton said on the conference phone. "Can you hear me okay?"

"Loud and clear, Bill," Leo said.

"You mentioned Carter Phillips toward the beginning of your talk and how, as a venture capital company, we should question our investment in Industrial Publications. You said your projections for the year don't look good and that cash is scarce. You're right that we want to make another acquisition. How do you propose to use the last two months of this year to improve profit and cash so we can execute our plans? All I heard you say was that pulling any cash out of the business wasn't likely to happen. I heard you talk about a long-term turnaround. Those are good things, but this year matters, too. Do you have a plan?"

Hal nodded profusely. Leo cringed. This was a one-on-one question, not one whose answer would benefit the employees in this meeting. On top of that, it embarrassed him. Leo wondered what Bill's intent was—whether he and Hal colluded to discredit Leo, or if Bill simply ignored the awkward dynamic he'd just created.

"Good question, Bill. I mentioned one of the reasons we're in the current predicament is the loss of some key people that were directly tied to revenue generation. We also lost our bookkeeper, who was a collections whiz. Her exit slowed down our cash procurement drastically. So, what I'd like to do in response is to do some immediate cost cutting."

Leo hoped Emily was taking notes on the promises he was about to make. When he turned his head in her direction, she immediately started clicking on her keyboard.

"We'll spread collections over a couple other admin people, plus we'll cut down on some travel," he said. "I'm shortening staff Christmas vacations and will be trimming bonuses to make up for some of the shortfall. Plus, we'll be cutting out the annual executive retreat in December, along with a few other expenses here and there."

"What will all these efforts produce in liquid cash at the end of the year?" Bill asked.

"We're tabulating and should have something for you soon."

Bill fell silent, apparently satisfied.

"I'm not sure what you're proposing is good enough," Hal said. "I've done preliminary calculations and that sort of strategy will maybe produce a couple hundred grand in cash. Part of the problem is we only have two months left in the year, and if we're going to do this, we should've started sooner." His eyes dared Leo to debate him.

"Another problem," Hal continued, "is that to enact some of what is being proposed would require immediate reinvestment of any capital we'd save, leaving next to nothing for CP. Bill and his mergers-and-acquisitions team would have to rely on the other companies in the portfolio to provide cash. This just isn't good enough."

The room froze. Leo's gaze shot to Will and Linda, neither of whom projected any confidence. Leo's mind generated several possible responses that collided in a jumbled mess. He needed to stall so he could think. "Of course it's not good enough. That's why we're having this meeting, why I'm laying bare the facts."

Will slid forward on his elbows. "Bill, I think we need a little more time to talk internally before we get back to you on that plan. Obviously, there's some disagreement."

"Oh, there's more than that," Hal shot back. "Your own boss admitted forty-five minutes ago in front of this group that our magazines have failed to successfully migrate to digital, and our website metrics leave much to be desired. We're barely able to keep up with all the upstarts launching blogs, magazines, content sites, and events. We're becoming irrelevant."

"I wouldn't go that far," Leo said.

"Of course you wouldn't," Hal shot back. "You haven't gone nearly far enough since you've been CEO. Bill, if we don't invest heavily in a turnaround, we won't survive. And if we invest according to Leo's plan, CP gets nothing to show for the hundreds of thousands they've pumped into this business, on top of the millions they shelled out to buy it three years ago. We're backed into a corner, and frankly anyone in Leo's position would be hard-pressed to pull out of it."

The edges of Leo's vision blurred as his mind hyper-focused on Hal. Had he just swiped at Leo only to turn around and redirect some of the blame *away* from him? Whose side was this guy on? Leo knew Hal wouldn't let the blame hang in the air. He would land it on someone, and land it hard.

"So, what do you propose?" Bill asked.

"Let me address the group for a minute before I answer that, Bill. We're all managers here, so I'm going to be blunt." Hal wielded his gaze like a tank turret around the room. "I want you all to understand that everything you hear is to remain in this group only."

"I agree," Bill said. Leo simply nodded. His leadership was eroding before his eyes, like the sand under his feet just a few short days ago.

Hal continued. "I propose three things. First, the state of our magazines, websites, and events falls squarely on the shoulders of our publisher. He's had plenty of time to turn them around, but instead they've continued to decline. So, I propose a publishing committee be formed. Sales, marketing, and audience development have traditionally fallen under the purview of one person, and it's not working. I want to split up those functions and let three equally powered VPs report up under me as part of my shift to overseeing operations."

"What—I'm going to become a sales manager?" Will blurted, slapping the table. "And you're going to become my boss? I don't think so."

Hal ignored him. "Bill, the three VPs will be named and will form the committee that will meet daily to coordinate strategy and daily tactics. The team will get more done more effectively in a shorter time than ever before."

Leo struggled for control—not just of the meeting, but of himself. He could feel his blood pressure rising; his fight-or-flight instinct squeezed his thoughts into an increasingly tiny space.

"Secondly," Hal continued, "I propose an accelerated cash recovery plan, similar to Leo's. I believe if he focuses much of his time on working with sales and directly with key accounts, we'll see our reserves fill back up quickly. Leo knows how to work with clients and is persuasive when dealing with their issues. I've seen him turn around troubled accounts."

Hal pushed from his chair and stood. Leo felt himself step back to protect his personal space, but knew he'd made a mistake when Hal smoothly stepped in front of him, partially blocking the group's view of their CEO.

"I'll support Leo in his efforts there," Hal said. "And Bill, I would add that as I move into more of an operations oversight role, I would recommend keeping Leo over admin, IT, and a few other areas."

"So what you're saying," Bill said, "is that you're going to become the co-CEO. I'm not sure I buy in to that."

"Not the case at all. Let me finish my proposal. The third prong is to execute my depreciation, tax, and debt restructuring plan. I've worked out how we can show 20 percent more profit this year, reduce our tax bill by a third through revenue deferral, and in the end conserve a quarter of a million in cash—minimum. Along with that, I plan on negotiating directly with our bank's president, a golfing friend of mine. I'll convince him to restructure our debt by converting our line of credit into a loan that gets refinanced with extended terms, effectively reducing our monthly payments by half of what they are now. We'll save another few hundred thousand next year."

Hal leaned over the table, pressing his palms on it. "I promise to return a million dollars to you in savings and newfound money in the next twelve months, Bill. It's either that or continue to let this place bleed. I'm giving you a concrete plan to turn this ship completely around and give CP some working capital toward your next acquisition. In fact, if you're open, I've identified two of our underperforming media properties that could be sold, generating another few million. And selling them won't hurt the rest of our media portfolio."

"You could guarantee that?" Bill asked.

"I could."

The entire room sat in silence. "Bill, I have a suggestion," Leo finally said. "Let's take this out of the public square and just the three of us talk. I have some thoughts, but I don't think it's appropriate to drag everyone else along until we get this figured out."

"Agreed," Bill replied. "You and Hal call me in fifteen minutes." He hung up.

Leo leaned against the edge of the table. "My apologies, everyone. This went in a different direction than I'd planned, which I guess is pretty obvious. For some of you it may be difficult to get your mind back on your work, but I'm asking you to do your best and I'll update you as soon as I can. This meeting is over."

He straightened and gave one last grin. "I apparently have another one to attend."

PART 5

Then you will know the truth, and the truth will set you free.

—John 8:32

Will, Linda, Susan, and Patrick stayed behind while the meeting broke up. Leo cut out before anyone could talk to him. As he watched Leo's back, Will thought, *Who can blame him?*

After the room emptied, Will shut the door and dropped into his chair. Patrick stared at his hands, while Susan nursed a tear and Linda looked out the window. Having this conversation was the last thing Will wanted to do.

"Let me tell you why I wanted you to stay," Will said. "Everyone is still in shock, and besides Leo himself, we're in the hottest seats in the company. The simple reason is we report to him. So if you care at all about your future, get your heads in the game right now and help me think this through. Susan," he said, startling her from her quiet sobbing. "Let's start with you. Give me your assessment. How do we defend against Hal's power grab? I'm still a little new here. What politics am I unaware of with corporate?"

Susan wiped her nose. "You don't get it," she whispered, shaking her head. "It's over. This is beyond politics. I've never seen anything like this."

"You want to know what I think?" Patrick demanded. He glared at Will. "I think *you're* the one in the hot seat. *You're* the one that needs to look for a job. Not any of us. Did you hear what Hal was saying? We got into this mess because of you. Leo can't take all the blame. It was your job to grow sales. Your job to build audience. Your job—"

"Patrick!" Linda snapped. "Enough."

Will put up his hand to echo Linda, but Patrick couldn't stop. "And speaking of jobs, Hal even told me I could keep mine after the smoke cleared."

"He did what?" Will said with a huge swallow.

"Yup. He seemed to know how this would turn out. And he was right." Patrick tilted his face toward the ceiling and closed his eyes.

"Oh, so not only are you blaming me for running the whole company into the ground," Will said, "but you're switching loyalties? Are you naïve enough to think he'll keep his promise? Grow up, kid."

Patrick still wouldn't make eye contact. Will had had enough of this idiot. "Do you know what you're really doing here?" he demanded. "You are conspiring with the one man trying to get us all fired. And you have the audacity to say *I'm* the reason for the entire company's problems? What about the competition? What about our parent company? What about the two salespeople that shredded their major accounts on the way out? What about *you*?"

"Guys!" Linda shouted, shoving her hands toward both of them. "Either you calm down and be civil, or Susan and I are leaving. You think this is helping Leo? You're just making it worse."

"We're done here," Will said. "Go ahead and leave. There's no being civil anymore." He pushed away from the table, slamming the floor with his feet and launching his chair into the credenza behind him. Coffee mugs crashed onto the floor. "We're done. And you, my friend," he said jabbing his finger toward Patrick, "are about to learn what it's like to be a casualty of war. Good luck with your career. And your life."

Will pushed through the door, banging it into the wall. In the otherwise quiet hallway, two employees scurried back to their cubes. Will knew his tirade had echoed and the rumor mill was already churning, but he didn't care. It had been overheating lately anyway.

He really was done. He wanted to run. He envisioned himself jumping in his car, squealing from the lot, heading back to Manhattan.

When he got to his office, he stared out the window. The world and all its opportunities beckoned him to leave this town and venture back into the job market. Even his sports car seemed out of place in the lot below.

But something kept him from leaving the building. One last piece of business remained undone.

Leo needed a moment. People were knocking, calling, texting. He responded to none of them. He craved silence so he could think.

What do I say to Bill? How do I deal with Hal? What do I tell Teresa if this conversation goes bad? His nerves failed to subside; if anything, they knotted up even more. The answer to all his questions remained a firm *I don't know.*

Which was the truth. He couldn't escape the fact that Hal had successfully executed a ruthless end run. The masterful stroke crippled Leo in front of everyone. During the upcoming phone conference with Bill, he considered thrusting the blame back on Hal, but Leo had already spread it among himself and his team. He knew no amount of persuasion or spin would change the outcome.

Then a novel thought struck him.

The truth. Just tell them the truth.

There was nothing else to say, anyway. Maybe it was time to throw himself on the mercy of Bill Grafton. Telling the absolute truth felt sort of freeing—no lies to remember, stories to concoct, or emotions to manipulate. What did he have to lose?

If he lost his job, he wouldn't die. If he walked out of here publicly humiliated, time would deaden the pain. If Teresa considered him a failure, he'd get another chance to prove his worth in another job. She wanted him to leave the company anyway. They couldn't take a simple vacation without this place wedging between them.

Some time off would be nice.

All because he would tell the truth.

When Leo emerged from his office, the world started closing in again. He didn't fight it. His clear conscience proved he had done all he could to save the company.

Emily, God love her, clutched her notebook under her chin like a shield. Her eyes sank into his. "Emily," he told his loyal assistant, "it's okay. Everything's going to be fine."

She bit her bottom lip. "I hear you say that," she said. "And I want to believe it. I'm trying."

"I know," he replied. She took a step to follow, but Leo stopped her. "Don't worry, you don't have to attend this meeting. I'll take good notes for you."

As he passed her, he detected a slight relaxing of her shoulders. She stood still and rubbed a moist eye, saying nothing.

He would stand alone, unlike most of his other meetings. Emily always wrote down details, helped him recall names, dates, and data, and by her simple presence encouraged him to lead boldly. But not today.

He resigned himself to whatever destiny had in store. But should he literally resign? Was that the fate that awaited him? Maybe such a preemptive strike would change the conversation, or at least ease his exit.

No, that would be a copout. Despite his defeat of the last hour, he felt confident in the truth. It stood on its own. It would hold him up. It would speak for him. And then if he was forced to resign, so be it.

He felt dozens of eyes as he walked along at an easy gait. Many staff members emerged from their offices and cubes to watch their humbled leader. He didn't care about his reputation now—that had been stripped from him, leaving nothing but a soft core, exposed and vulnerable.

He felt closer to these people now that he had come out from behind his façade. The fog had lifted between them, revealing him to be nothing more than a man struggling under failure. He knew many of them had tasted failure too, whether in their working or personal lives, and in a strange way he felt relieved that they saw him as a real person.

He started returning some of the gazes, seeing them with new eyes. Their expressions spoke more than any amount of words. Each face, he realized, housed a world of emotions that had risen, dipped, and twisted like the most savage of rollercoasters today. And the ride wasn't over.

He felt for them all. He realized their lives were just as messy as his, probably more so. They had their own stresses, fears, joys, and sorrows. They all wondered about their careers and what their futures held.

Leo felt the weight of all of this, and his soul was heavy. His surrender to truth had done something to his mind and his whole inner being. His vision was clearer, as if he could finally see outside himself and into the lives of his people. They all dealt with their own families, bills, marital issues, long hours at the office, sicknesses, and past regrets.

He felt ashamed at his constant efforts at self-preservation. At the lost opportunities for bettering the lives of all these people. He had squandered his position as CEO and wished he could start over.

The open conference door at the end of the hall beckoned to him. It was time to end this and move on to the next phase of his life. Only one more painful meeting. Then the healing could begin.

Will stood next to the door like a bar bouncer. As Leo approached, he noticed the young man's red eyes. Will looked tired and defeated himself.

"Leo, can we talk before you go in?"

"Of course."

"I know this is a closed meeting, but we all know what it's about. I just wanted to shake your hand." Will's fingers trembled until he clasped Leo's hand in a tight grip. "And I also wanted to tell you a few things real quick. Please hear me out."

Leo waited. He heard a door open and close inside the conference room.

"Leo, you know I'm loyal to you. You hired me. I've been behind you since day one and I'm still in your camp. Just wanted to make sure you knew that."

"I do," Leo said. "I've never questioned your loyalty."

"Good. I didn't want you to go in there feeling alone. No matter what happens, I'm with you." Will stepped away from the door. He sighed as if his words resisted him. "I promised I'd never desert you without giving you a chance to change my mind. Remember that?"

"Yep. And I remember agreeing to it."

"Well, today I'm expanding our agreement." He clenched his teeth. "If you leave, I leave. If you stay, I stay. That's it."

Leo looked at the closed door. He put a hand on his friend's shoulder. "I take that as a huge, undeserved compliment, Will." He reached for the handle. "Thanks. Really. It means more than you know."

Despite the shadowed room, Leo felt lighter than he had in months. He closed the door softly behind him.

Hal sat across the table. The military man smirked as if he'd already won. Hal leaned forward and held his fingers above the speaker phone's keypad. "He's waiting for our call. Anything you want to talk about before I dial?"

Leo shook his head. He took his time snagging a bottle of water from the wet bar. He grabbed a glass and filled it with ice, then flipped on another light above the sink. When he took a seat on the other side of the phone, Hal had finished dialing.

After one ring, Bill's voice broke over the line. "You both there?"

"We are," Hal said.

"Good. Let's continue where we left off. Hal, you were talking about cleaning house and still working alongside Leo. How would that work?"

"Well, as I said, he would keep admin, IT, and key-account sales," Hal said. "I don't have much experience in those areas, and I'd need someone like Leo to handle them."

"Someone like him," Bill cut in, "which implies some-one other than him?"

Hal shook his head slightly and looked right at Leo. "I don't have anything against you personally, Leo. But we can't let things keep going the way they are. I want to replace some people and restructure. Simple as that. I didn't think you'd want to stay and take a demotion. How can you expect to keep your job in its current form, based on your results?"

Leo held up one hand. "I didn't say anything. It's your proposal."

"And one I haven't bought into yet," Bill said. Hal looked at the phone, obviously surprised. Bill sighed. "Guys, this is just a bad situation all the way around. Before I give you my decision, I want to hear from Leo how we got here."

"How we got here, sir?"

"Yes. And you can cut the 'sir.' I want you to talk to me as if you're explaining it to someone on your team. It's just us here. Give me the truth behind the façade. This is your last chance to make your case."

Leo leaned forward. "I don't really have a case to make. But I do have more of the truth for you."

"Then let's hear it."

Leo hesitated, then a surge of confidence propelled him. "It's my fault. I failed to execute. I didn't perform, and I let you and the staff down. That's it."

He didn't know how to interpret Bill's silence. The seconds dragged on. Was Bill expecting more? Was he shocked and disappointed? Hal folded his hands under his chin.

"If I said anything else, it would be an excuse," Leo continued. "You heard me give all the surface reasons in the meeting, but when it comes down to it, Hal's right. I admit my role in our downturn. I'm the leader, and this happened on my watch. So I'm ready to be reassigned into the marketplace, if that's what you want."

More silence, though still no reaction.

"I can tell you this, Bill. If you keep me on, I will throw myself into the game and execute the turnaround. I'll work alongside Hal. I'll throw out my strategy and start from scratch. I'll do whatever it takes. I'd just ask that you let me do the restructuring of my staff, or at least heavily influence it."

Hal was looking at him now, his blank stare revealing that he hadn't expected this capitulation. He remained tight-lipped.

"Well," Bill began, "this is interesting."

Interesting? Leo turned his ear toward the phone. He'd never heard the man use that word.

"I have to say, young man, this changes things." Bill audibly exhaled.

Leo fell quiet. He and Hal both sat dazed.

"I have someone else here with me," Bill said. "I apologize for not letting you know until now, but he wanted to remain anonymous." Shuffling sounds came across the line. "I'll let him speak for himself."

"Hello, gentlemen." The voice was vaguely familiar to Leo. "Christopher Hilton here. Sorry for not alerting you about my presence on the call, but I had my reasons, which I'll explain." Hilton's voice carried a slight British or Australian accent. "Leo, we've met, but I haven't yet made Hal's acquaintance."

Without waiting for returned niceties, Christopher continued. "As you know, I've been hanging around for a while, purportedly as a consultant. I've been observing, listening, and spending a lot of time with the board. I've gotten to know you and your company extremely well for one reason: to decide whether to acquire Industrial Publications."

Leo choked on his water.

"And I've finally made a decision. Bill, the most recent terms we discussed are acceptable. You can draw up the final agreements and schedule a closing."

Leo leaned back in his chair. *What just happened here?*

"I know this is a shock," Christopher continued. "This is a surprise to Bill right at this moment, too. We've been in talks for some time, but to be honest, I didn't make my final purchase decision until just now. Let me tell you why.

"I've needed a media company about your size to add to my portfolio. You're in markets that are meaningful to me. But rather than look at bottom-line profitability, I first looked at revenue, then at the leadership. Net profit didn't matter all that much. The reason I've hesitated was to assess you, Leo."

"I'm sorry, sir? Assess me?"

"Up until now, I wasn't sure you were the man to lead the company going forward. I didn't want to bring in anyone from the outside—the chances for success are lower with outside CEOs. And I didn't see anyone else in the company I wanted in your slot. If you weren't the leader, the deal was off. What gave me hope all along was that your people—most of them, anyway—are loyal to you and respect you. If you didn't turn the corner like you did, I would've crossed you and Industrial Publications off the list."

"If I may ask, what corner was that?"

"In the last few minutes, you showed immense integrity and courage—qualities I want in my CEOs. You admitted your faults, took responsibility for failure, and were prepared to be let go. You deferred to authority."

Leo's hand shook. "I'm not sure what to say."

"I understand," Christopher said. "To me, character is everything in leadership. Always has been. Bill, let me hand it back to you. I'll let you execute the first condition of our agreement now."

"Christopher, I have to say it's hard to pull one over on me, but you did it with flying colors," Bill said. "I thank you. I'll convey your verbal assent to the board and we'll turn the agreements around to you forthwith. We have a deal."

"Gentlemen," Christopher said, "it's been a pleasure."

A moment later Leo heard the sound of a closing door and more rustling on the line. "I've never had a deal turn out like this," Bill said. "Ever."

He sighed before moving on. "You two are probably wondering about next steps. The condition he mentioned has to do with personnel changes. Hal, I'm sorry, but I'm letting you go, effective immediately. There will be a few other separations in addition to yours. I assure you this isn't personal between me and you. It's entirely Christopher's call, and I agreed to effect these changes before he took over."

"Wait a minute." Hal jumped forward. "Can't we at least wait until after the closing? And may I ask why he singled me out?"

"It's simply a term of the deal. A letter of intent has been signed, and an even stronger intent contract was executed contingent on this call."

"You can't be serious," Hal said. "Doesn't he see that my strategy will work? How can he possibly—"

"All I can tell you is he's very particular about personnel. To be blunt, he didn't want you working with Leo anymore. The battle between you two has hurt the company over the past year, and while I wouldn't have made this decision, it's his prerogative. His style apparently meshes more with Leo's. Who knows what else is on his mind? But he was adamant about this change."

Hal slammed the table and stood. "This is ridiculous. Absolutely ridiculous." He paced the floor, glaring at Leo and the phone. "This company is headed for the edge of a cliff. And Hilton thinks the old leadership that got IP into this mess can save it? You've got be kidding me."

"I'm afraid this is where we are," Bill said.

"Fine." Hal held out his palms and backed away. Words escaped him. He opened and shut the door with such force that a painting bounced off the wall. The thud rumbled down the hallway.

Leo realized he'd been holding his breath. "He's gone, Bill. Just us in the room now."

"Leo," Bill began, quickly regaining his calm. His tone dropped some of its formality. "I know this has been an ordeal for you. I'm sorry for that. It's been hard for all of us. If this company survives, it'll be a miracle, but that's not really my concern anymore."

"Understood."

"Can I ask you a question?" he asked. "A personal one."

"Of course."

"I didn't recognize the Leo Perkins on this call versus the one I heard in the management meeting or in my limo. What changed? Did you just get desperate and throw in the towel?"

"I really don't know," Leo said. "But it happened right before I came in here. I realized all I had left was the truth."

"What do you mean?"

"I didn't want to fight anymore. The only thing I had left in the bag was the God-honest truth—what I really felt, deep down. Yeah, I guess you could say I got desperate. My fate was out of my hands for the first time in my life."

"Well, whatever it was, Christopher noticed. As soon as you finished your little speech, he virtually stole the phone from me. Apparently, that was all he needed to hear. You want some advice, son?"

"I need all the help I can get."

"Stick with the truth. Your new boss thrives on it. It'll get you far with him."

"I will."

"One more thing. Christopher wants to meet with you. He's actually heading to the airport and wants to have dinner with you and your wife."

"When?"

"Tonight."

When Leo opened the conference room door, Linda and Will's faces were the first to greet him. He didn't say anything at first, and they didn't ask right away; a shared glance followed by a nod to each of them led to slowly building smiles.

"It's over," Leo said. "It's all over."

"And?" Will demanded. "Are we staying or going?"

"We're all getting another chance."

Linda beamed. "We could tell by Hal's scowl on his way out. Not to mention we heard him through the walls before he about tore the door off its hinges. Congratulations, Leo."

"I'm still in shock."

"Any details for us?" Will asked.

"One big one." Leo leaned against the wall to steady himself. "We're being bought by Christopher Hilton, the consultant you've heard about. He consummated the deal just now on the phone. And he's flying here tonight to have dinner with me and Teresa."

"I've been hearing about him for sure," Will said. "A real up-and-up guy. Lots of media experience. And tons of family money."

"What about Hal?" Linda asked. "Is he leaving?"

"He's gone. Gathering his stuff now. No more battles, guys."

The three slowly headed down the hall. Patrick, Susan, and a dozen other employees emerged from their offices and cubes. Leo walked in a dream state. He let Will spread the news.

One staffer started clapping. Several more joined him, soon adding a few cheers. The din drew more people from their desks until they lined the hallway.

Leo savored the relief washing over him. One of his knees shook as he walked. He stopped to catch his balance and leaned close to Linda's ear. "What was that verse again? The one about the bird."

She grinned. "'Like a fluttering sparrow or a darting swallow, an undeserved curse does not come to rest.' Proverbs 26, verse 2. There's a lot more where that came from."

"I just might have to read it for myself. You have an extra Bible?"

Linda nodded. "I'll have one on your desk in the morning."

When they reached Leo's office, he opened the door and pulled his phone out. "Right now, I've got to call my wife. I need to let her know we've got a dinner date with the new boss."

Teresa grabbed Leo's hand. Her soft touch blended with the dim lights and the flickering candle on their table. Clinking china and muted voices surrounded them, creating an oasis more relaxing and reassuring than any beach. Gourmet aromas mixed with the scent of the flowers in front of them.

"They were a nice touch, weren't they?" Leo remarked, turning the vase. "Do you know what kind they are?"

"Looks like jasmine," Teresa said. "They're beautiful." She ran her fingers across the arrangement and took in the aroma. "This was thoughtful of Christopher. You know, tonight I don't mind waiting. It's actually sort of nice sitting here with you. We haven't done this in a while."

Leo put his arm around his wife's shoulders. "I know." He pulled her closer. "And I'm sorry. I promise we're going to do more of it."

"You sure you can promise that?"

He smiled. "I'll do my best. Though I do have a feeling Christopher's going to be a little more understanding when it comes to family. There's something about him."

"What kind of something?"

"The way he looks at the world—it's just different."

She put her head on his shoulder and squeezed his hand. "I can go with that."

Relief washed over Leo every time he thought through the day's events. He knew more challenges were waiting, but for now, in this moment, he relished this new calm in his soul. He looked forward to the food and conversation with Christopher Hilton. This was a man he could follow. He barely knew him, yet Leo's loyalty for him blew past anything he'd felt for Bill.

"I hope I'm not interrupting anything," a smoothly accented voice said. Christopher approached the table with a grand smile. His blond hair sloped back in neat waves and a set of bright teeth lit up his face. At least six feet tall, he wore a pinstripe suit and took off his coat as he gestured toward an empty chair. "May I join you good people?"

Leo rose and extended his hand. "Sir, it is a pleasure and an honor. I want to thank you — "

"It is I that must do the thanking," he replied. He shook Leo's hand heartily. "But first I must meet your lovely wife. Teresa, it is *my* honor to finally make the acquaintance of the woman behind a man I have come to respect."

She shook his hand and smiled broadly. "Mr. Hilton, you have just warmed my heart even more, if it were possible. I can see great things ahead for you two."

"Please, it's just Christopher. And indeed you are correct about the future. I have some plans I'm going to share with you tonight that I think you'll like. Please, sit."

After further pleasantries and completing their dinner orders, Christopher leaned forward and clasped his hands. To Leo, the conversations at neighboring tables dimmed as the smooth voice of his new boss commanded his attention.

"I want to apologize for something," Christopher began. "I led you on a surreptitious path over the past several days that was confusing and misleading. But it was necessary for two reasons. First, I needed to know who you were, Leo. I needed to understand what was deep inside you. They say what pours out of someone under duress is what they're filled with at their core. You passed that test. At the very end there, I saw what's inside you. I saw humility and a willingness to take the blame for failure. I saw perseverance and passion.

"Secondly, I wanted to know how you thought. I wanted to hear your strategy for the company's turnaround. Despite the results of the past few years, I liked your plan, but more importantly I liked your leadership style. You had some difficult people around you that made your job difficult. Hal gave you no quarter. His proposed turnaround plan sounded good, but honestly, it's what most companies do when they get a new leader. I can show you how to do the same things he proposed and how to manage it through your team.

"But I'm getting a little ahead of myself. Before we get down to business, I'd like to ask you something, Leo."

"Anything."

Christopher rested his gaze on the candle for a moment. "Will you forgive me for disrupting your life?"

Leo squeezed Teresa's hand under the table. A smile—a true smile—flowed naturally onto Leo's face. "Of course," he said. "It wasn't fun, and definitely not painless, but at the end of the day it was worth it. I have no hard feelings whatsoever."

Christopher's face brightened as he returned the grin. "Excellent, my friend. I'm happy to hear that," he said. "Now, where was I?"

EPILOGUE

Hal Perrone sat in his car long after pulling into the garage. He'd never expected to be here at the end of a workday, with no job to go to in the morning. The silence reminded him of the finality of the day's events—and the shock.

He didn't know what to do with the silence. It ate at him like acid.

Nevertheless, he sat. A heaviness of the soul pressed him into his seat. What would he find inside, anyway? Just a quiet house, devoid of life. Reminders of glory past—ribbons for distinguished military service, pictures of his long-gone parents sitting on their porch in Italy, various plaques and trophies from a life of incessant competition.

Regrets would welcome him home, today's disaster chief among them. The failure sapped his will to move. He didn't even want to think. Maybe a bottle and sleep would do him good.

He closed his eyes. Not only had he failed in his bid for the CEO slot, his efforts had cost him his job, and very possibly his career. Who would hire an ousted fifty-two-year-old CFO in today's market? Though he'd deftly survived the last regime change at Industrial, this one had attacked from the shadows.

The garage's ceiling light switched off, startling him. The only light left was the setting sun's dim orange glow through a single window.

His phone vibrated in his coat pocket. He pulled it out. It was Bill. What was there left to say after his callous firing just a few hours earlier? Hal didn't answer. He wasn't ready to talk to anyone, let alone the man who had just ruined his life.

He rested his head against the seat, staring at the orange patch of light crawling up the wall. He lost focus as his mind wandered into exhaustion. When he snapped to, the glowing mass had moved a good foot higher. Maybe he wouldn't need the bottle after all.

The quick doze brought some clarity back to his mind. He turned the phone over in his lap and noticed Bill had left a voice mail. He punched it up and put it on speaker.

"Hal, it's Bill. I know you don't want to talk to me right now, if ever. But I think what I have to say may change your mind. The bottom line is this. Hilton's acquisition of IP has given Carter Phillips the cash it needs to make another acquisition, with plenty left over. I'm buying out my partners. And I've got another target in sight, this one in accounting software. It needs a CEO who knows finance and can take the product to the next level. This company has huge potential, and I want someone I trust to take the helm. Call me if you're interested."

Bill fumbled with the phone as if hanging up, then his voice came back on the line. "And keep your chin up, marine. Time to move forward."

Twelve months later, Leo sat in his office, alone for the first time all day. He pondered the enthusiastic response in the all-staff meeting he'd just led. Comments like "That was the best meeting we've ever had" and "I love my job" hung in his mind. He'd never heard such positive feedback after a meeting.

How did I get here? For the first time in years—perhaps a decade—he was having fun at work. The company had stabilized and showed signs of budding growth. Winter was over. Most of the bad apples were gone.

For sure, much work remained: IP's structure needed a revamp, a few siloed departments needed to be shaken up and combined, and old processes required overhauls. The financials still limped along. Next year's budget awaited a thorough rethink.

But the work had given his lead team renewed purpose. They were getting things done. They smiled and joked with each other. Replacing the drama and politics with forward momentum infused new enthusiasm into the workplace. No longer did fear force everyone into survival mode. The exodus of staff and clients had calmed down.

Leo rested his hands behind his head, spinning his chair to face the window. The late afternoon sun lit up the picture frames on his credenza. Teresa smiled at him from his favorite photo; his kids beamed with love for their dad. A cut-glass industry award from years ago cascaded miniature rainbows onto the floor.

Leo felt at home and at peace in this place. He knew more trials were ahead, but he sensed a quiet strength building in himself. It manifested as an intense care for the people he led—to protect them, ensure a healthy working environment, motivate them with a vision of the future, and help them grow. He wanted to treat them like the family that stared back at him right now.

The door opened softly behind him. He wheeled around.

"Linda," he said. "Good to see you."

"Sorry to barge in," she said, "but I tend to take open-door policies literally. One of my faults, I guess."

"Not at all. What's going on?"

"I just wanted to swing by for a couple minutes. Lately I've felt compelled to come in and encourage you with something, but I've kept putting it off. Today he wouldn't let me hit the snooze button again. So here I am."

"He?"

"Yeah, well, God. He's been prompting me to let you know that I've been praying for you ever since I gave you that Bible."

Leo didn't think long before replying. "First, thank you," he said. "And secondly, I can tell you it's working. Something's changing in me, and definitely changing around here. Please keep it up."

"I'd be happy to."

"And I want you to know I've been reading that Bible. I've been especially intrigued by Jesus's life and leadership. He was quite a man. I'm still processing all of it."

Linda seemed to ponder her next words.

"I saw Patrick today," she said. "His new marriage is really agreeing with him. But if you remember, he thought about asking that young lady to marry him for a year before he got the guts to take the plunge. Now, he wonders what took him so long. If you think about it, you can only process the Bible for so long, Leo. At some point, you have to decide."

"Decide?"

"What you believe about Jesus."

The sun brightened through the window, filling the room with its presence. He reclined in his chair. Linda was so perceptive, wise in her own way. He respected her connection to God—and realized he wanted it, too.

Leo Perkins suddenly understood where the peace in his soul had been coming from.

"I think I have."

AFTERWORD: SEEING REALITY

Blessed are the eyes that see what you see.
—Luke 10:23

Has your life ever been disrupted the way Leo's was?
Bill Grafton's threats were the first shock to his system; then Hal rattled him with a frontal attack. Desperation gripped him until capitulation seemed the only way out.

Leo's desperate surrender to authority, and his reliance on the saving power of truth, brought him a peculiar peace. He felt free to stop fighting; he could envision life beyond failure. A heartfelt vulnerability emerged from his ruined ego.

Only then did Christopher make his move.

This mysterious investor had been in control the whole time, manipulating even Bill. Christopher watched and waited while Leo's character revealed itself. Satisfied that his man had suffered enough humiliation and finally saw the value and power of truth, Christopher revealed his plans for Leo—more than the beleaguered CEO could've ever imagined.

This, of course, resembles God's ways with us.

GETTING TO THE HEART

Without a close walk with the Lord, we look at life through glasses so discolored and fogged that we only catch glimpses of reality. Our vision is stained by the sin in ourselves and others. It's also clouded by the façades other people want us to see and the stories they want us to believe.

Only God knows what's really going on inside people. As Acts 1:24–25 teaches, the Lord alone knows people's hearts. In the story you just read, you had this kind of omniscient view into the main characters:

- Susan saw everything as a source of pain, fear, and disaster.
- Linda knew the Lord would direct her steps no matter what happened, and that she had a higher purpose than just her job.
- Hal's unhealthy ambition morphed into more insidious intentions. James 3:16 says, "For where you have envy and selfish ambition, there you find disorder and every evil practice."

- Will's ambition and loyalty warred against each other, leading to his own transformation when the latter won out.
- Patrick wanted to save himself. His survival instinct drove his every thought, word, and action. If he lost this job, he feared his whole life would fall apart.
- Leo, of course, wanted to save the company in order to preserve his reputation.

Is it possible to get this kind of internal perspective of the people we lead? Can we somehow bypass their filters and façades and get at their hearts? It would be nice if we could see these realities more often.

I believe we can.

STRIKING DEEP

Christopher told Leo, "They say what pours out of someone under duress is what they're filled with at their core." Observing Leo during the crisis told Christopher everything he needed to know about how Leo would likely act in the future. Was he willing to admit failure? Would he try to cover up his mistakes?

While Christopher's method certainly works, there is a less painful way to discover someone's heart: God's Word. When applied in the right way, it helps us see unfiltered reality in people. It cuts through their outer shells:

> Hebrews 4:12: "For the word of God is alive and active. Sharper than any double-edged sword, it penetrates even to dividing soul and spirit, joints and marrow; it judges the thoughts and attitudes of the heart."

The foundational step for leaders who want to employ the Word is to let it soak into their own minds and hearts first before bringing it to bear with others. This comes through study, prayer, and a relationship with Jesus Christ.

DEVELOPING DISCERNMENT

As we study the Bible, we learn how to detect the motivations behind people's words and actions. Following are some examples of wisdom from Proverbs:

1. *Outward cues can reveal the state of someone's thoughts.*

    Proverbs 15:13: "A happy heart makes the face cheerful, but heartache crushes the spirit."

    Proverbs 14:30: "A heart at peace gives life to the body, but envy rots the bones."

    Proverbs 27:19: "As water reflects the face, so one's life reflects the heart."

2. *Verbosity and folly are brothers.*

Proverbs 15:14: "The discerning heart seeks knowledge, but the mouth of a fool feeds on folly."

Proverbs 10:8: "The wise in heart accept commands, but a chattering fool comes to ruin."

Proverbs 12:23: "The prudent keep their knowledge to themselves, but a fool's heart blurts out folly."

3. *Humility and self-control lead to honor.*

Proverbs 22:11: "One who loves a pure heart and who speaks with grace will have the king for a friend."

Proverbs 18:12: "Before a downfall the heart is haughty, but humility comes before honor."

If you want more of this pithy wisdom, try reading Proverbs with a highlighter in hand!

SIN-STAINED GLASSES

Regardless of how clearly leaders see the horizon, clouds are bound to roll in. Some days we just feel foggy. Our leadership can fall flat because of mood, sickness, criticism, or just plain fatigue.

The biggest cloud over our leadership is sin. It darkens us from the inside out, drowning out our connection with the Holy Spirit.

Though he didn't know it at the time, Leo fell victim to a wave of sin in himself and others. People's selfish fear, greed, bitterness, malice, envy, and ambition swirled around him. It broke apart the unity of the team and nearly sank the company.

This kind of sin comes naturally to people. Even the apostle Paul couldn't escape it:

Romans 7:21: "So I find this law at work: Although I want to do good, evil is right there with me."

The first law of sin is that it never leaves us. Second, the Holy Spirit enables us to see it for what it is: an unavoidable aspect of human nature. Third, he enables us to recognize sin and fight against it with truth and love. As Peter says, "Love covers over a multitude of sins" (1 Pet. 4:8).

Finally, the gospel closes the book on sin. Jesus defeated it. He was the perfect sacrifice, "in whom we have redemption, the forgiveness of sins" (Col. 1:14).

As leaders, we must deal with our own sin by trusting in Christ's redemption. And we must ask the Holy Spirit to help us fight its effects in those around us.

A FINAL WORD ON REVEALING REALITY

As we said earlier, God probes everyone's hearts. He not only knows what we're thinking, but judges our deepest desires:

Proverbs 16:2: "All a person's ways seem pure to them, but motives are weighed by the LORD."

Because the Lord knows everyone so well, we can ask him to reveal information about the people around us. I often pray silently for insights while I'm talking with someone, especially when they come to me for advice. He answers by dropping a helpful thought or question into my mind.

Jeremiah 33:3: "Call to me and I will answer you and tell you great and unsearchable things you do not know."

Not only does the Lord unveil secrets, he gives us words:

Proverbs 16:1: "To humans belong the plans of the heart, but from the LORD comes the proper answer of the tongue."

I pray this book has opened your eyes to the spiritual realities of leadership. We don't have to fall victim to people's invisible motives. No longer do we have to succumb to their worries and fears. Not when we have an omniscient, loving Father who enjoys showing us truth.

Like Leo at the end of the story, we can rest in the power of this truth. We don't have to wonder what to say; we simply speak what is true, and during the times we're still at a loss for words, we ask the Lord to speak through us.

May you speak his words, think his thoughts, and lead with his true vision.

> *Once more Jesus put his hands on the man's eyes. Then his eyes were opened, his sight was restored, and he saw everything clearly.*
> —Mark 8:25

QUESTIONS FOR DISCUSSION

1. Have you ever watched political intrigue unfold in your office? How did you respond?

2. In the first part of the book, what did you think of Leo as a leader? How did your opinion change by the end?

3. What is the overriding leadership principle you learned from this book?

4. Whether an employee or a boss, do you think you're doing a good job of explaining your expectations to coworkers? How can you improve?

5. Have you ever worked with a domineering personality like Hal? What did you learn that can help you for the rest of your career?

6. Which character in this story do you most identify with? Which of their weaknesses do you share, and what should you do to improve them?

7. Have you ever asked the Holy Spirit to remove your colored glasses and let you see what he sees in people?

8. Which Bible verse or verses reviewed in the afterword do you see as having the most direct application in your life right now?

ACKNOWLEDGMENTS

Through Colored Glasses fulfills more than a desire to write a leadership fable—it marks the launch of DeepWater Books, a new publishing imprint I've been dreaming about for years. Our mission is to create practical and inspiring books designed to deepen people's walk with God. Leadership is our starting point, with other topics to follow.

Speaking of a deeper walk with God, Networld Media Group, DeepWater's parent company, has been a sanctifying tool in my life for many years. I am a better man and leader because of its challenges and successes, especially meaningful to me as the company approaches its twentieth anniversary.

I thank Kathy Doyle, a trusted friend and president of Networld. The Lord brought you to this business, Kathy, to take us to the next level. You have certainly done that and more. I appreciate your encouragement to chase this book publishing dream I've been nursing since I was a teenager!

Kent Evans, your infectious joy and inspiring creativity have encouraged me more than you know. I cherish our coffee brainstorms and deepening friendship. You were the force behind my quest for a better title for this book. Thank you for not letting me settle for mediocrity. Your comments on an early draft of the manuscript helped me see blind spots in the story. The book is better because of you.

Karen, you are a wife of such noble character and wisdom—not to mention creativity and excellence in everything you do. Thank you for staying up late with me generating titles! You often broke through my discouragement with innovative ideas, kind words, and a gentle touch. Thank you for your prayers, patience and love.

And to my Lord, I offer humble thanks for lifting my eyes to see the clear, unfiltered truth of salvation in Jesus alone.

ABOUT THE AUTHOR

Tom Harper is CEO of Networld Media Group and publisher of BiblicalLeadership.com, a free online source of encouragement, tips, and how-to for leaders seeking to apply biblical principles in their daily lives. Tom lives in Louisville, Kentucky, with his wife and three children. He is the author of *Leading from the Lions' Den: Leadership Principles from Every Book of the Bible* (B&H, 2010).

BiblicalLeadership.com is a new online resource
with free tips, ideas, and encouragement
to help leaders follow God's ancient wisdom.

For leaders in:

Church | *Business* | *Education* | *Non-profit*